The Red B

Cindy Harris
Illustrated by Anthony Carnabuci

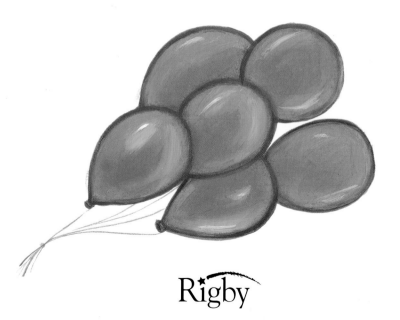

Rigby

The red balloons fly over the park.

3

The red balloons fly
over the hill.

The red balloons fly
over the store.

The red balloons fly over the school.

9

The red balloons fly
over the water.

The red balloons fly over the trees.

The red balloons fly over the house.

15

The red balloons fly over me!